NEIL A. KJOS
PIANO LIBRARY

LEVEL FIVE

PIANO REPERTOIRE

SELECTED & EDITED BY

Keith Snell

Etudes

THE NEIL A. KJOS PIANO LIBRARY

The **Neil A. Kjos Piano Library** is a comprehensive series of piano music in a wide variety of musical styles. The library is divided into eleven levels and will provide students with a complete performance experience in both solo and ensemble music. Teachers will find the carefully graded levels appropriate when choosing repertoire for evaluations, auditions, festivals, and examinations. Included in the **Neil A. Kjos Piano Library:**

Preparatory Level - Level Ten

Fundamentals of Piano Theory
Piano Repertoire: Baroque & Classical
Piano Repertoire: Romantic & 20th Century
Piano Repertoire: Etudes
Scale Skills
Essential Piano Repertoire
Music of the 21st Century
New Age Piano
Jazz Piano
One Piano Four Hands
Music for Christmas

PREFACE

Piano Repertoire: Etudes from the **Neil A. Kjos Piano Library** offers piano students graded studies for the development of technic, style and musicianship. Used in conjunction with ***Baroque & Classical*** and ***Romantic & 20th Century***, ***Etudes*** provides pianists with additional music by composers of the 17th - 20th centuries in an assortment of styles, each piece precisely selected to reinforce the technical requirements found in the corresponding collections. The carefully graded levels ensure steady and thorough progress as pianists advance in their study of etudes.

Compact disc recordings are available for each volume in the ***Piano Repertoire*** series. Recorded by pianist Diane Hidy, the interpretations follow the editions closely as practical examples for students. Each CD includes all three volumes from the ***Piano Repertoire*** series at each level: ***Baroque & Classical***, ***Romantic & 20th Century***, and ***Etudes***.*

*Preparatory and Level One are included on one CD.

CONTENTS

ISBN 0-8497-6231-6

Etude I

Carl Czerny
(1791-1857)

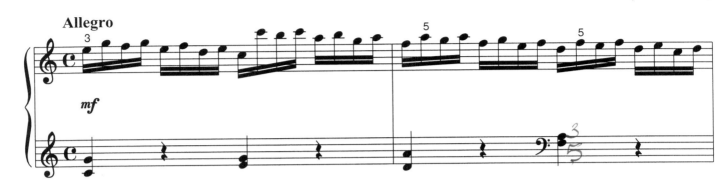

Etude II

Carl Czerny
(1791-1857)

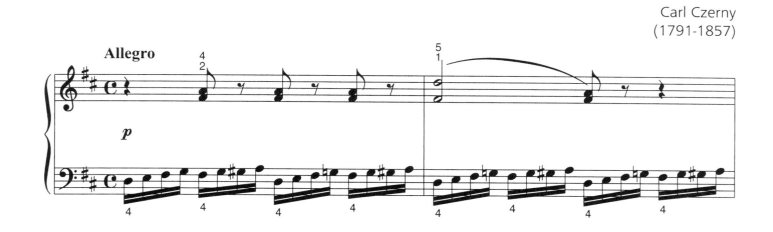

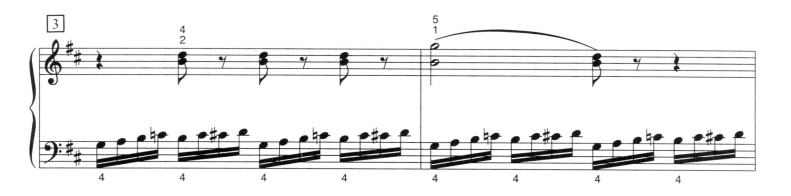

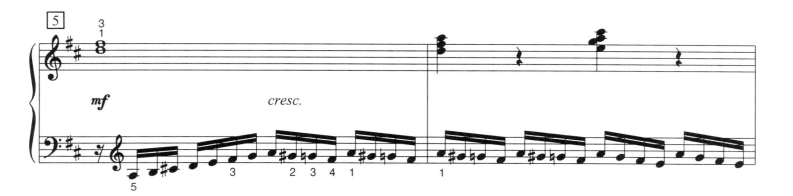

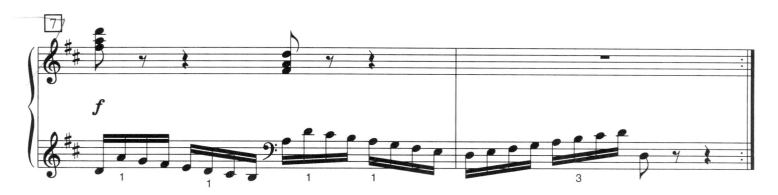

© 1997 Neil A. Kjos Music Company, 4380 Jutland Drive, San Diego, California, 92117.

Etude III

Carl Czerny
(1791-1857)

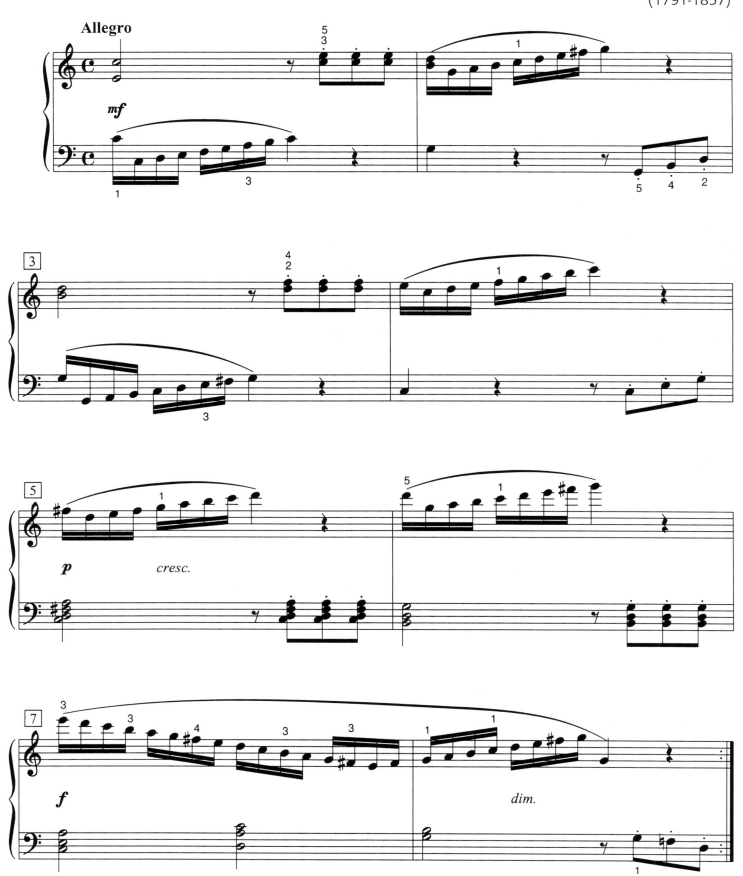

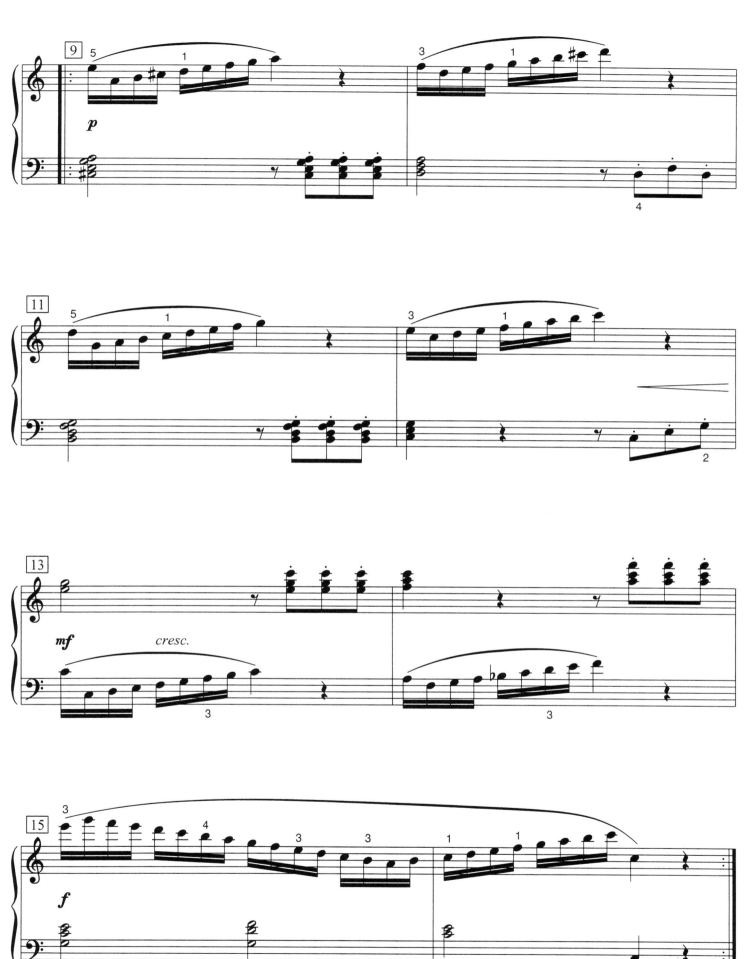

Tarantella

Op. 100, No. 20

Friedrich Burgmüller
(1806-1874)

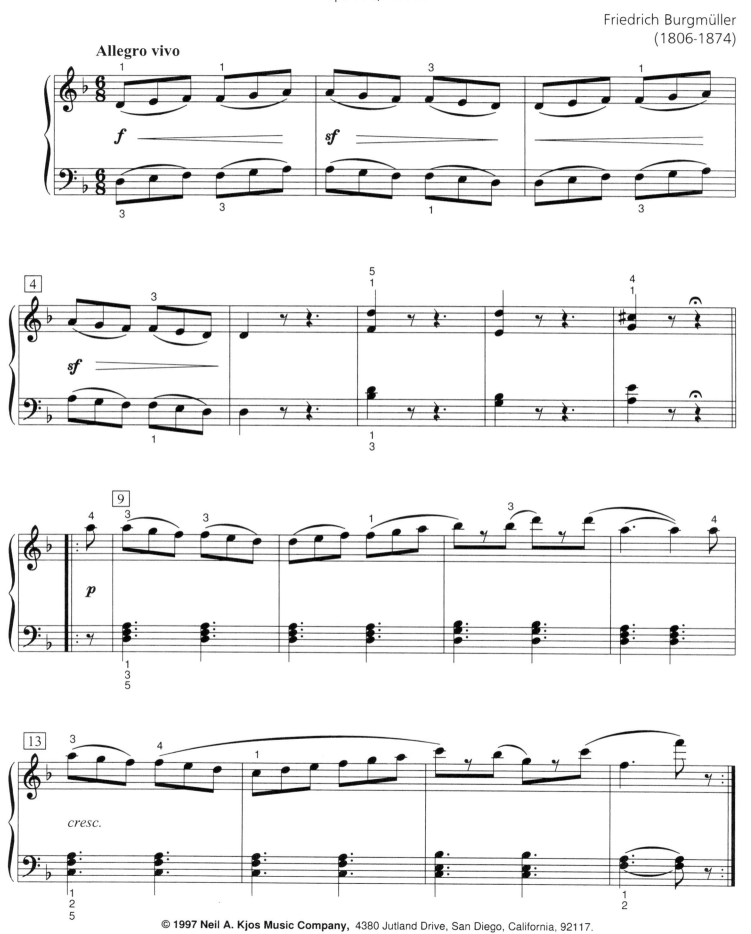

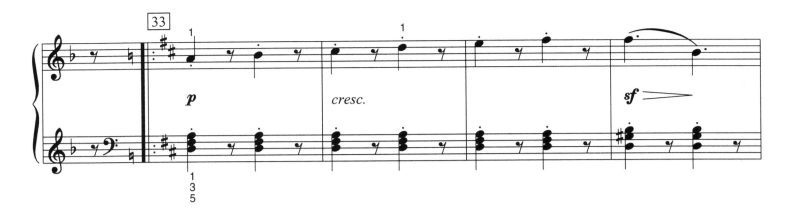

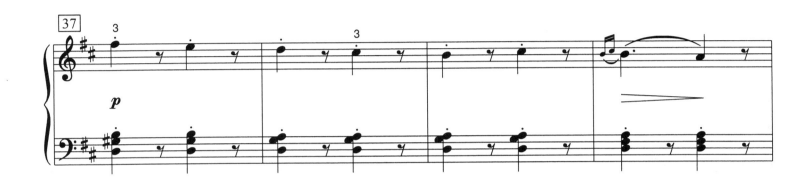

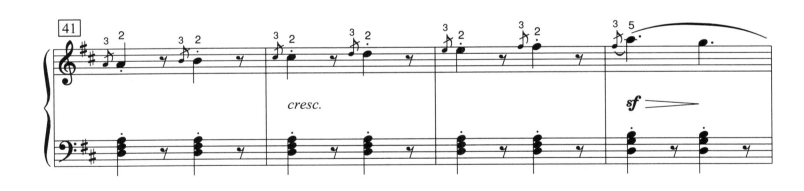

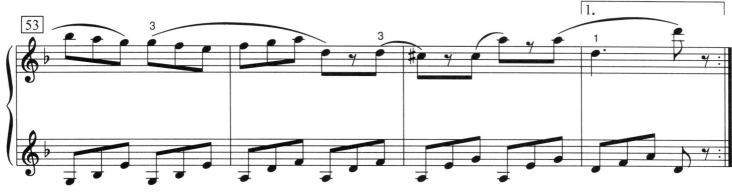

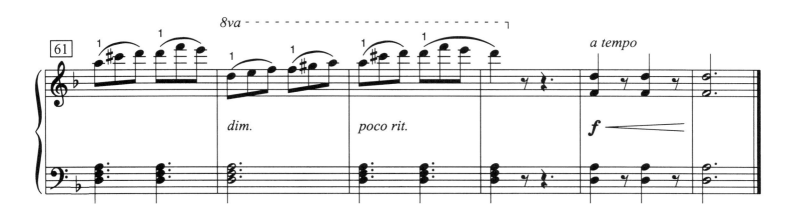

The Return

Op. 100, No. 23

Friedrich Burgmüller
(1806-1874)

Molto agitato quasi presto

13

GP645

The Swallow

Op. 100, No. 24

Friedrich Burgmüller
(1806-1874)

The Farewell
Op. 100, No. 12

Friedrich Burgmüller
(1806-1874)

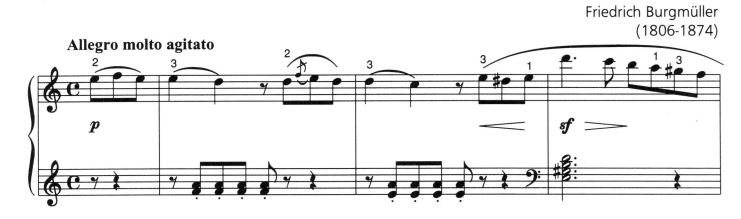

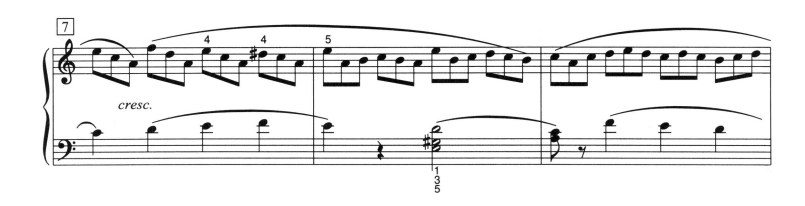

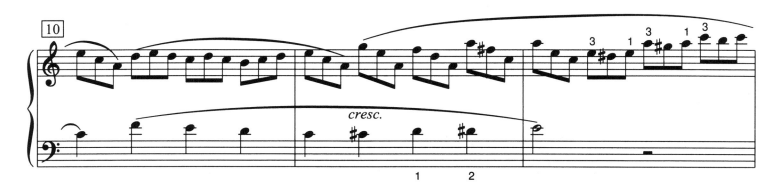

Avalanche

Op. 45, No. 2

Stephen Heller
(1814-1888)

20

Curious Story

Op. 138, No. 9

Stephen Heller
(1814-1888)

The Orphan

Op. 64, No. 4

Jean Louis Streabbog
(1835-1886)

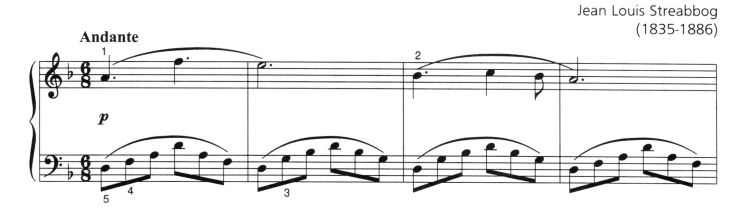

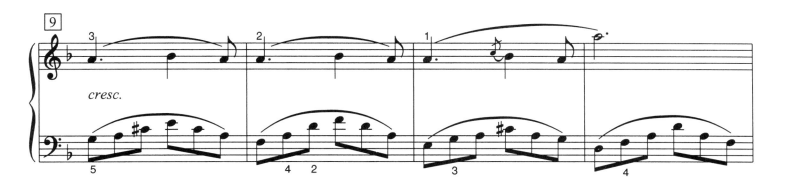

Little Etude

Op. 68, No. 14

Robert Schumann
(1810-1856)

Leise und sehr egal zu spielen
Lightly and very evenly

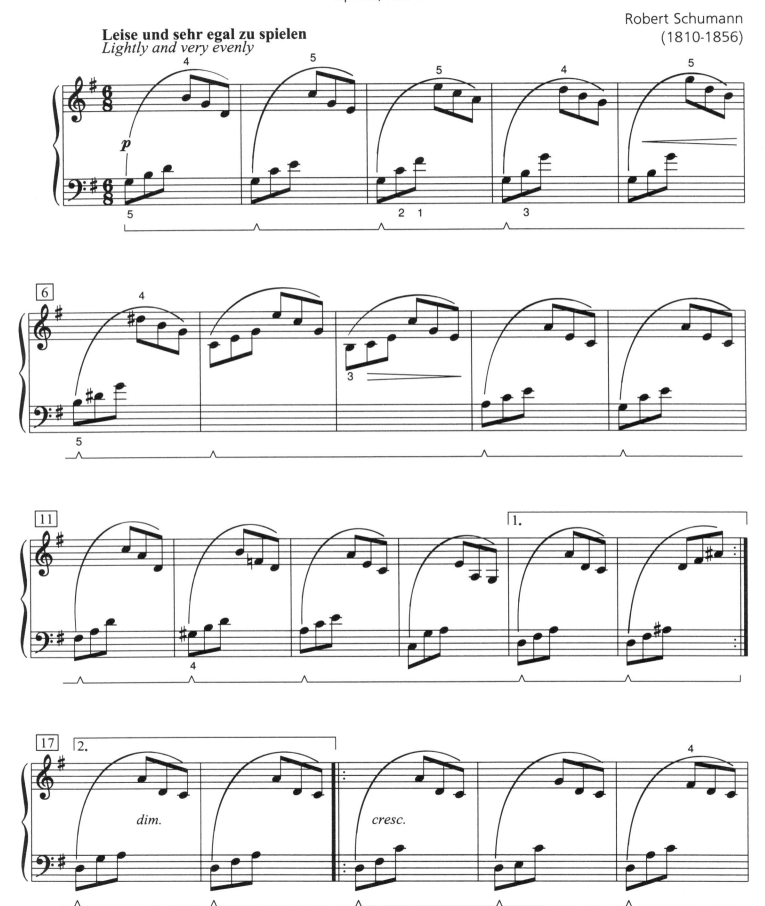

* The notes in small print are Schumann's suggestion for alternate performance.
The editor recommends playing the alternate version when repeating this section.

Etude in A Minor

Op. 27, No. 3

Dmitri Kabalevsky
(1904-1987)

COMPOSER BIOGRAPHIES

Friedrich Burgmüller (1806-1874), German composer, came from a musical family. He moved to Paris in 1832 where he enjoyed a considerable reputation as a pianist, composer, and piano teacher. Burgmüller is particularly noted for his three sets of etudes for piano: Op. 100, Op. 105, and Op. 109.

Carl Czerny (1791-1857) Austrian composer, pianist and teacher. He was a favorite piano student of Ludwig van Beethoven, and he was the teacher of Franz Liszt. Czerny's fame as a piano teacher of unusual ability had spread by the time he was only sixteen years old. He frequently held student piano recitals in his parents home in Vienna. Beethoven attended these recitals often, and eventually entrusted Czerny with the musical education of his nephew. Czerny was a prolific composer. He published more than one-thousand works including symphonies, overtures, concertos, chamber music, songs, choral music, and church music. However, he is best known for his hundreds of volumes of teaching pieces and etudes for piano.

Dmitri Kabalevsky (1904-1987) Russian composer, began to play the piano by ear when he was six years old, but he did not begin formal lessons until he was fourteen. When he was twenty-one he entered the Moscow Conservatory and was such a brilliant student that upon graduation he was invited to become Professor of Composition. In addition to composing and teaching, Kabalevsky was a conductor, music critic, musicologist, and toured as a pianist. He wrote many different kinds of music: symphonies, concertos, ballets, chamber music, advanced piano pieces, and also music for radio, movies, and stage plays.

Robert Schumann (1810-1856), German composer and pianist, wrote his first piano pieces when he was seven. In 1832, Schumann injured his hand and began to devote his energies to composition rather than playing the piano. In 1840 he married Clara Wieck, a brilliant pianist who performed many of Schumann's works. Schumann wrote about other musicians as a critic in his magazine, *The New Music Journal*; he was the first to report on the importance of Chopin and Brahms. In 1850 Schumann was appointed Musical Director for the city of Düsseldorf. He held that position until 1853 when mental illness compelled him to resign. His compositions include symphonies, many piano works, a piano concerto, chamber music, songs and choral works.

Louis Streabbog (1835-1886) French pianist and composer. He wrote hundreds of piano pieces, many of which were for his students. His last name was actually Gobbaerts, but he prefered to publish his music under the name Streabbog — Gobbaerts spelled backwards.